Reading for M

M000248390

Grade 2

Table of Contents

S-11046 Homework Helpers—Reading for Meaning 2
ll rights reserved—Printed in the U.S.A.
opyright © 1995 Frank Schaffer Publications, Inc.
3740 Hawthorne Blvd., Torrance, CA 90505

his book is a compilation of Frank Schaffer's
oxed Activity Cards FS-3133.

ISBN #0-86734-815-1

Colors

One word in each sentence has mixed up letters.
Write all the sentences the correct way.
Use the Word Bank.

Word Bank

black   yellow
blue   red
orange   green

1. My apple is dre.

2. My horse is kblac.

3. The grass is eegnr.

4. The sky is buel.

5. A banana is leylwo.

6. An ronaeg is good to eat.

Write your answers below.

Numbers

One word in each sentence has mixed up letters.
Write all the sentences the correct way.
Use the Word Bank.

Word Bank

five	two
nine	four
seven	one

1. I have owt eyes.

2. I have fvei toy cars.

3. Three is smaller than rouf.

4. I have nnie pet fish.

5. Do you have eno nose?

6. There are sveen days in a week.

Write your answers below.

FS-11046 Homework Helpers—Reading for Meaning 2

All Mixed Up

Write each sentence so it makes sense.
Don't forget the periods.

1. are teeth My white very.

2. large are elephants The.

3. I my love pet bird.

4. have You smile such a nice.

5. ten and Five five are.

6. will I do my best very.

Write your answers below

FS-11046 Homework Helpers—Reading for Meaning 2

Sequencing Sentences

Write the directions in the correct order.

Watch the funny clowns.

Go to the circus.

Smile and laugh.

Listen for a friendly hello.

Pick up the telephone.

Dial the number.

Write your answers below.

FS-11046 Homework Helpers—Reading for Meaning 2

Find the Word

Write these sentences. In place of *cucumber*, add a word that makes sense. Use the Word Bank.

Word Bank

stars	garage
sing	Brush
bike	football

1. We drove the car into the cucumber.

2. The cucumbers are in the sky.

3. Let's cucumber to Dad.

4. Cucumber your teeth every day.

5. I love to ride my cucumber.

6. Throw me the cucumber.

Write your answers below.

FS-11046 Homework Helpers—Reading for Meaning 2

Cucumbers

Write these sentences. In place of *cucumber*, add a word that makes sense. Use the Word Bank.

Word Bank

sleep	telephone
friend	animals
sun	dog

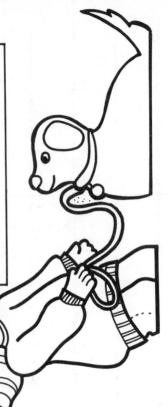

1. Be kind to cucumbers.

2. Get eight hours of cucumber.

3. Call me on the cucumber.

4. My best cucumber is Janet.

5. A cucumber is a good pet.

6. The cucumber is in the sky.

Write your answers below.

© Frank Schaffer Publications, Inc.

Name That Word

Write these sentences. In place of *cucumber*, add a word that makes sense. Use the Word Bank.

Word Bank

mouse	see
ring	milk
Sunday	bug

1. I cannot cucumber in the dark.

2. Monday comes after Cucumber.

3. A glass of cucumber tastes good.

4. A bell can cucumber.

5. A cucumber loves to eat cheese.

6. A cucumber has six legs.

Write your answers below

FS-11046 Homework Helpers—Reading for Meaning 2

Putting Words in Order

Write these sentences in another order so they make sense. Don't forget the periods.

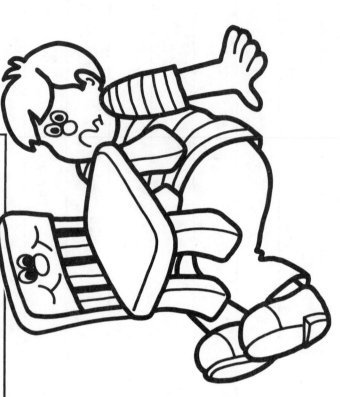

1. The sky is in the sun.

2. A chair sat on a boy.

3. Zoo are in the animals.

4. The green is very grass.

5. Apples loves to eat Jim.

6. The sea is in the whale.

Write your answers below.

Word Order

Write these sentences in another order so they make sense. Don't forget the periods.

1. My Mary is name.

2. This funny is very book.

3. The car is in the girl.

4. Two and one are one.

5. Lunch a good eat.

6. My bed is in my teddy bear.

Write your answers below.

Silly Sentences

Write each sentence so it makes sense.

1. I love hot ice cream.

2. I like cold chicken soup.

3. A rabbit sings.

4. A stop sign is green.

5. Let's fly to the park.

6. A ball is square.

Write your answers below.

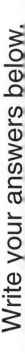

10

Funny Sentences

Write each sentence so it makes sense.

Crunch!

1. Dan rides his hat.

2. I like to swim in a tree.

3. My girlfriend is Jim.

4. We eat rocks for lunch.

5. My pet whale lives in a cage.

6. The sun shines at night.

Write your answers below.

FS-11046 Homework Helpers—Reading for Meaning 2

Scrambled Sentences

Write each sentence so it makes sense.
Don't forget the periods.

1. have two I eyes.

2. ten I have fingers.

3. ears have two I.

4. I have bellybutton one.

5. I eyes with see my.

6. hear with I ears my.

Write your answers below.

FS-11046 Homework Helpers—Reading for Meaning 2

What's the Word?

This is fun. Write these sentences so they make sense. Use the Word Bank.

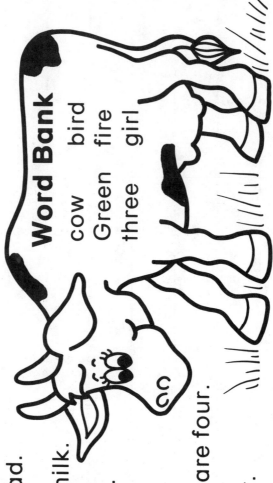

Word Bank

cow	bird
Green	fire
three	girl

1. A _____ can read.

2. A _____ gives milk.

3. A _____ can fly.

4. A _____ is hot.

5. One and _____ are four.

6. _____ is a color.

Write your answers below.

Pull-Out Answers

Page 1
1. My apple is **red**.
2. My horse is **black**.
3. The grass is **green**.
4. The sky is **blue**.
5. A banana is **yellow**.
6. An **orange** is good to eat.

Page 2
1. I have **two** eyes.
2. I have **five** toy cars.
3. Three is smaller than **four**.
4. I have **nine** pet fish.
5. Do you have **one** nose?
6. There are **seven** days in a week.

Page 3
1. My teeth are very white.
2. The elephants are large.
3. I love my pet bird.
4. You have such a nice smile.
5. Five and five are ten.
6. I will do my very best.

Page 4
Go to the circus.
Watch the funny clowns.
Smile and laugh.

Pick up the telephone.
Dial the number.
Listen for a friendly hello.

Page 5
1. We drove the car into the **garage**.
2. The **stars** are in the sky.
3. Let's **sing** to Dad.
4. **Brush** your teeth every day.
5. I love to ride my **bike**.
6. Throw me the **football**.

Page 6
1. Be kind to **animals**.
2. Get eight hours of **sleep**.
3. Call me on the **telephone**.
4. My best **friend** is Janet.
5. A **dog** is a good pet.
6. The **sun** is in the sky.

Page 7
1. I cannot **see** in the dark.
2. Monday comes after **Sunday**.
3. A glass of **milk** tastes good.
4. A bell can **ring**.
5. A **mouse** loves to eat cheese.
6. A **bug** has six legs.

Page 8
1. The sun is in the sky.
2. A boy sat on a chair.
3. Animals are in the zoo.
4. The grass is very green.
5. Jim loves to eat apples.
6. The whale is in the sea.

Page 9
1. My name is Mary.
2. This book is very funny.
3. The girl is in the car.
4. One and one are two.
5. Eat a good lunch.
5. My teddy bear is in my bed.

© Frank Schaffer Publications, Inc.

Pull-Out Answers

Page 10
Answers will vary. Possible responses:
1. I love chocolate ice cream.
2. I like hot chicken soup.
3. A rabbit hops.
4. A stop sign is red.
5. Let's walk to the park.
6. A ball is round.

Page 11
Answers will vary. Possible responses:
1. Dan rides his bike.
2. I like to swim in a pool.
3. My girlfriend is Julie.
4. We eat sandwiches for lunch.
5. My pet parrot lives in a cage.
6. The star shines at night.

Page 12
1. I have two eyes.
2. I have ten fingers.
3. I have two ears.
4. I have one bellybutton.
5. I see with my eyes.
6. I hear with my ears.

Page 13
1. A **girl** can read.
2. A **cow** gives milk.
3. A **bird** can fly.
4. A **fire** is hot.
5. One and **three** are four.
6. **Green** is a color.

Page 14
1. A **dog** can bark.
2. A **cloud** is white.
3. A **plant** has leaves.
4. A **fish** has fins.
5. A **bee** can buzz.
6. The **sun** shines.

Page 15
Wake up in the morning.
Get dressed.
Go to school.

Open the toothpaste.
Put toothpaste on the brush.
Now brush your teeth.

Page 16
Put on your socks.
Put on your shoes.
Tie your shoes.

Toast some bread.
Butter the toast.
Eat the toast.

Page 17
Pick up the bat.
Hit the ball.
Run to first base.

Get the shopping cart.
Put the food in the cart.
Pay for the food.

Page 18
Go to the zoo.
Pay at the gate.
See the animals.

Find a book.
Open the book.
Read the book.

Pull-Out Answers

Page 19

Open the door.
Go outside.
Play ball outside.

Pick up a banana.
Peel the banana.
Eat the banana.

Page 20

1. My best color is orange.
2. My pet dog can jump high.
3. Is the sun in the sky?
4. I love peanut butter.
5. Stop at the red light.
6. Five and one are six.

Page 21

1. A turtle is a slow animal.
2. Put your shoes on your feet.
3. The ice cream goes in your mouth.
4. A birthday party is fun.
5. It's good to have a friend.
6. Please brush your hair.

Page 22

1. Eggs can't grow on trees.
2. A kite flies in the sky.
3. Clouds are white.
4. Always do your best.
5. I cannot see my neck.
6. A cow gives milk.

Page 23

1. I have a name.
2. This is funny.
3. Dinosaurs are big.
4. Books help you.
5. The sun shines on me.
6. Keep our school clean.

Page 24

1. The moon is like a ball.
2. Can a banana be green?
3. I sleep in a bed.
4. Let's play after school.
5. Catch the ball.
6. I brush my teeth.

Page 25

Answers will vary. Possible responses:
1. The mouse ran past the baseball.
2. The bluebird built a nest.
3. The dinosaur is taller than that big tree.
4. Six ants walked across the rug.
5. A whale lives in the ocean.
6. I played with my teddy bear and a ball.

HOMEWORK AWARD

presented to

_____

for successfully completing
this Homework Helper Book

_____
signed

_____
date

D

FS-11046 Homework Helpers—Reading for Meaning 2

Read and Think

This is fun. Write these sentences so they make sense. Use the Word Bank.

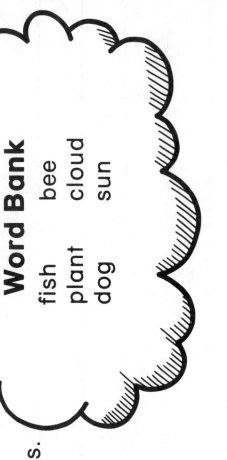

Word Bank

fish	bee	cloud
plant	dog	sun

1. A _____ can bark.

2. A _____ is white.

3. A _____ has leaves.

4. A _____ has fins.

5. A _____ can buzz.

6. The _____ shines.

Write your answers below.

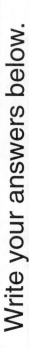

14

Putting Sentences in Order

Write the directions in the correct order.

Now brush your teeth.

Put toothpaste on the brush.

Open the toothpaste.

Go to school.

Wake up in the morning.

Get dressed.

Write your answers below.

One, Two, Three

Write the directions in the correct order.

Tie your shoes.

Put on your shoes.

Put on your socks.

Eat the toast.

Toast some bread.

Butter the toast.

Write your answers below.

16

What's the Order?

Write the directions in the correct order.

Hit the ball.

Pick up the bat.

Run to first base.

Pay for the food.

Get the shopping cart.

Put the food in the cart.

Write your answers below.

17

First, Second, Third

Write the directions in the correct order.

Open the book.

Read the book.

Find a book.

See the animals.

Go to the zoo.

Pay at the gate.

Write your answers below.

Sentence Order

Write the directions in the correct order.

Eat the banana.

Peel the banana.

Pick up a banana.

Go outside.

Open the door.

Play ball outside.

Write your answers below.

FS-11046 Homework Helpers—Reading for Meaning 2

© Frank Schaffer Publications, Inc.

One Word Does Not Belong

This is tricky. A word in each sentence does not belong. Write each sentence correctly.

1. My best color is orange six.

2. My pet dog tree can jump high.

3. Is the sun horse in the sky?

4. I love peanut milk butter.

5. Stop at the red green light.

6. Five and three one are six.

Reasoning

Write your answers below.

20

Find the Word That Does Not Belong

This is tricky. A word in each sentence does not belong. Write each sentence correctly.

1. A turtle is a slow fast animal.

2. Put your shoes on your head feet.

3. The ice cream goes in your nose mouth.

4. A birthday party is sad fun.

5. It's good to have a cold friend.

6. Please brush your eyes hair.

Write your answers below.

FS-11046 Homework Helpers—Reading for Meaning 2

Which Word Does Not Belong?

This is tricky. A word in each sentence does not belong. Write each sentence correctly.

1. Eggs can can't grow on trees.

2. A car kite flies in the sky.

3. Apples clouds are white.

4. Always do don't your best.

5. I cannot see my hands neck.

6. A cow car gives milk.

Write your answers below.

22

Tight Squeeze

Write these sentences. Please leave a space between each word.

1. Ihaveaname.

2. Thisisfunny.

3. Dinosaursarebig.

4. Bookshelpyou.

5. Thesunshinesonme.

6. Keepourschoolclean.

Write your answers below.

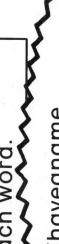

23

Squeezed Together

Write these sentences. Please leave a space between each word.

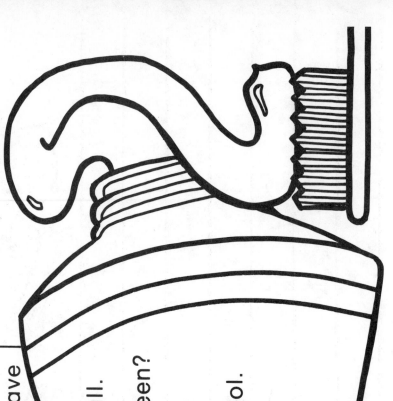

1. Themoonislikeaball.

2. Canabananabegreen?

3. Isleepinabed.

4. Let'splayafterschool.

5. Catchtheball.

6. Ibrushmyteeth.

Write your answers below.

FS-11046 Homework Helpers—Reading for Meaning 2

Lots of Luck

Can you write a sentence using **dog** and **hunt**?
You might write: **A dog will hunt for a bone.**
Now please write a sentence for each group of words.
Lots of luck!

1. baseball * mouse

2. nest * bluebird

3. dinosaur * big tree

4. rug * six ants

5. whale * ocean

6. teddy bear * a ball

Write your answers below.

FS-11046 Homework Helpers—Reading for Meaning 2

Homework Helper Record

Color the circle for each page you complete.

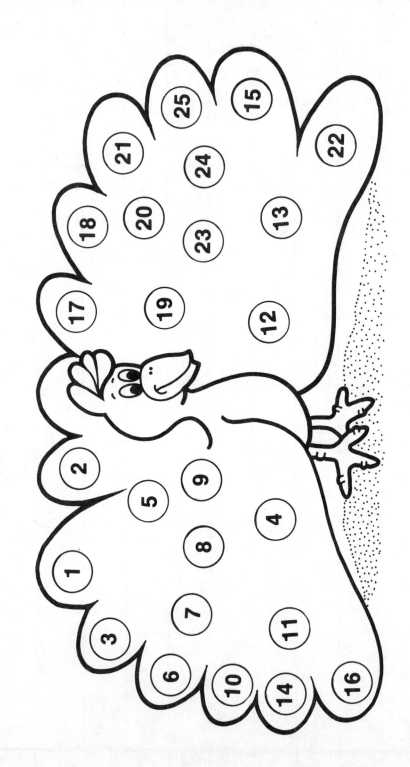